Angels We Have Heard o

Gloria

w. Flute 8'
t. Principals 8', 4', and 2'; Mixture
ed. 16' and 8'

accel.

ff

accel.

ff

Be Strong in the Lord

Strength

Sw.   Flutes 8' and 4'
Gt.   Principals 8', 4', and 2'
Ped. 16' and 8'

TOM FETTK

Arranged by Crystal Davis Cla

14

Be Strong in the Lord — 5

Redeemed, How I Love to Proclaim It

Redeemed

Sw.   Solo Reed 8'
Gt.   Flutes 8', 4', and 2'
Ped. 16', 8', and 4'

WILLIAM J. KIRKPATRICK
Arranged by Sharon Elergy Rogers

18

19

Redeemed, How I Love to Proclaim It — 4

20

Easter People, Raise Your Voices

Regent Square

Sw.   Solo 8'
Gt.   Principals 8', 4', and 2'
Ped. 16' and 8'

HENRY T. SMART
Arranged by Gayden Sikes

24

26

28

How Great Our Joy

Jüngst

Sw. Flutes 8' and 2'
Gt. Flutes 8', 4', and 2'
Ped. 16' and 8'

Traditional German Melody
Arranged by Anna Laura Page

How Great Our Joy — 2

How Great Our Joy — 4

55

How Great Our Joy — 9

Carols Sing
Bethlehem Song

Sw.   Flutes 8', 4' and 2'
Gt.   Flute 8'; Principals 4' and 2'
Ped. 16', 8', and 4'

MARTHA PUCKETT
Arranged by Donna Williams

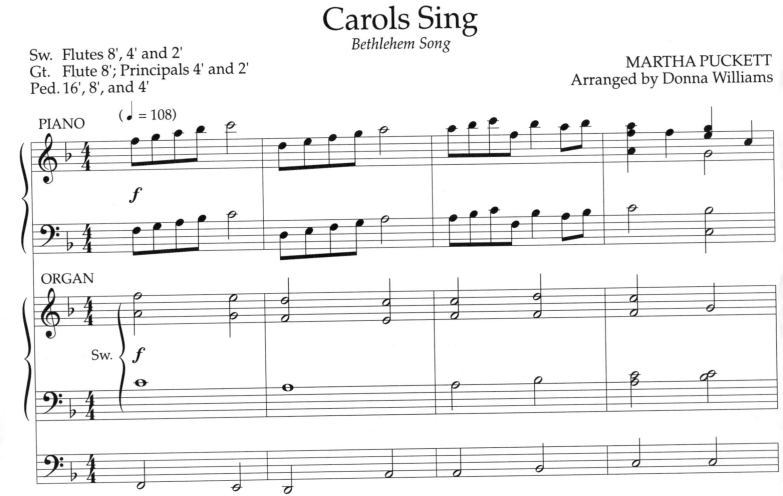

Carols Sing — 2

40

Carols Sing — 3

42

Carols Sing — 5

Father, Son, Holy Spirit

Jackson

Sw. Strings
Gt.   Flutes 8', 4' and 2'
Ped. 16' and 8'

MARK BLANKENSHIP
Arranged by Gayden Sikes

*"Chorus of the Blessed Spirits," from *Orfeo*, by Gluck.

Father, Son, Holy Spirit — 2

46

Father, Son, Holy Spirit — 3

Father, Son, Holy Spirit — 6

50

It Is Well with My Soul

Ville du Havre

Sw. Flutes 8' and 4'
Gt. Solo Reed 8'
Ped. 16' and 8'

PHILIP P. BLISS
Arranged by Ken Denton

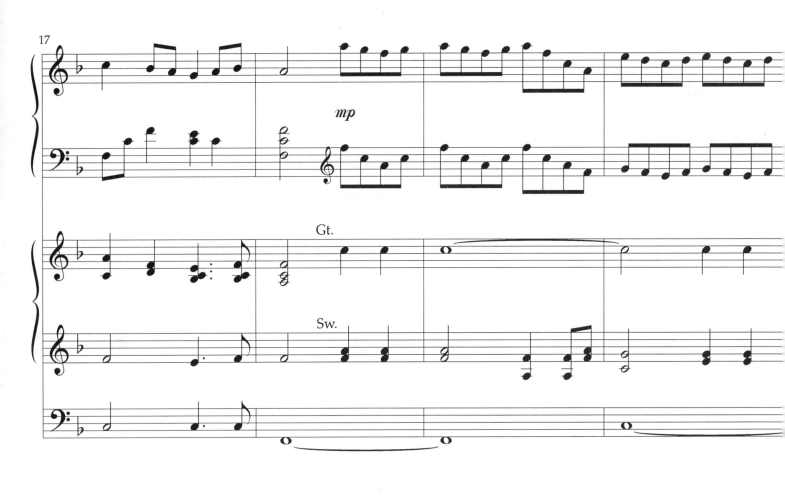

56

Add Principal 2'

ff

ff

f

mp

Nearer, Still Nearer

Morris

Mrs. C. H. MORRIS
Arranged by Todd Spangler

Sw. Solo 8'
Gt. Flutes 8' and 4'
Ped. 16' and 8'

Nearer, Still Nearer — 7

Hymns of Praise

Arranged by Anna Laura Page

Sw. Flutes 8' and 2'
Gt. Principals 8' and 4'
Ped. 16' and 8'

*Tune, St. Denio, Welsh Hymn Tune.

*Tune, To God Be the Glory, William H. Doane

72